My House

Jan Swartz and Adria F. Klein

Illustrated by David House

🎠 Dominie Press, Inc.

Publisher: Raymond Yuen
Series Editor: Stanley L. Swartz
Consultant: Adria F. Klein
Editor: Bob Rowland
Designers: Lois Stanfield and Debra Dickerson
Illustrator: David House

First published 1996
New Edition © 2002 Dominie Press, Inc.

Published by:

₽ Dominie Press, Inc.

1949 Kellogg Avenue
Carlsbad, California 92008 USA

www.dominie.com

Dominie Level	Early Intervention	Guided Reading	DeFord Assessment
I	I	A	I B

Softcover Edition ISBN 1-56270-469-9
Library Bound Edition ISBN 0-7685-2555-1

Printed in Singapore by PH Productions Pte Ltd
2 3 4 5 6 PH 05 04 03

I can see my door.

I can see my window.

I can see my roof.

I can see my chimney.

I can see my porch.

I can see my garage.

I can see my mailbox.

I can see my house.